Contents

Hello, Harry!

Harry is in a **muddle**. Like lots of children, he has new things to learn. He's finding that he can't always have everything he wants, and that being **honest** is sometimes hard.

YOU Choose

Hand it Over, Harry

Don't Steal

Sarah Eason

It might be useful for parents or teachers to read our 'How to use this book' guide on pages 28–29 before looking at Harry's dilemmas. The points for discussion on these pages are helpful to share with your child once you have read the book together.

First published in 2011 by Wayland

Copyright © Wayland 2011

Wayland
338 Euston Road
London NW1 3BH

Wayland Australia
Level 17/207 Kent Street
Sydney, NSW 2000

Produced for Wayland by Calcium
Design: Paul Myerscough
Editor for Wayland: Camilla Lloyd
Illustrations by Ailie Busby

British Library Cataloguing in Publication Data

Eason, Sarah.
    Hand it over, Harry! Don't steal.—(You choose!)
    1. Theft—Juvenile literature. 2. Theft—Juvenile fiction.
    I. Title II. Series
    364.1'62–dc22

ISBN: 978 0 7502 6643 7

Printed in China

Wayland is a division of Hachette Children's Books,
an Hachette UK company.
www.hachette.co.uk

Follow Harry as he finds himself in tricky situations in which he must choose to be **honest**.

Make Mum happy, Harry

It's Harry's Mum's birthday tomorrow.

Harry wants to give her
a present, but he hasn't
got any **pocket money.**

What should Harry choose to do?

Should Harry:

a take a bar of chocolate from a shop without paying for it?

b pick some flowers from his neighbour's garden?

C make his Mum
a special card?

Harry, choose **C**

It's not the present that's important, it's showing Mum how much you love her. She would be really unhappy if she knew that you had taken something that wasn't yours.

What would YOU choose to do?

Learn to share, Harry

Harry has been playing
at his friend's house.

His friend has got
the best digger EVER
and Harry wants to
take it home.

What should Harry choose to do?

Should Harry:

a break it so his friend can't play with it either?

b ask if he can **borrow** it for the weekend if he's really careful?

c hide the digger under his coat and take it home?

Harry, choose **b**

Being friends is all about **sharing**, not keeping things for yourself. You should ask before you borrow something. If you ask nicely, you will find that most people are happy to share with you.

What would YOU choose to do?

Take it back, Harry

Harry is at the shops and he's **bored**.

He cheers himself up by trying on sunglasses. When he leaves the shop, he **realises** that he's still wearing a pair.

What should Harry choose to do?

Should Harry:

a put the sunglasses on his little brother?

b tell his Mum and ask her to come back to the shop with him?

c take off the **price tag** and pretend they were always his?

Harry, choose **b**

It's much better to own up to a **mistake**. Grown-ups do understand. And it's okay to ask someone to stay with you if you're scared of owning up.

What would YOU choose to do?

Be truthful, Harry

Harry is riding his
bike at the park
near to his house.

A man walks
past and drops
some money
by accident.

What should Harry choose to do?

Should Harry:

a shout 'Excuse me!' and tell the man he has dropped his money?

b put his wheel on the money to hide it and then pick it up when the man has gone?

c pick up the money and then pedal off really quickly?

Harry, choose **a**

You shouldn't keep things that aren't yours, even if you really want to. The man will think you are an extremely good boy for giving back his money, and you should feel very **proud**.

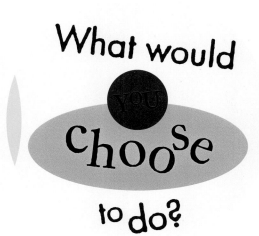

What would **YOU** choose to do?

Earn it, Harry

Harry's Nanna says
he can have a biscuit.

As Harry reaches for the biscuit jar, he sees a big pile of coins on the shelf. Harry hasn't got any money and wishes that he did.

What should Harry choose to do?

23

Should Harry:

a put two coins in his pocket – Nanna won't notice that they've gone?

b take half of the coins and buy Nanna a present?

c take a biscuit and ask Nanna if he can earn some pocket money while he's visiting?

Harry, choose **c**

Taking money without asking is **stealing**, even if you do plan to buy presents with it. But **earning** money makes you feel good, and Nannas usually love to find little jobs that you can do.

What would **YOU** choose to do?

Well done, Harry!

Hey, look at Harry! Now he has made honest choices, he's feeling much **happier**.

Did you choose the right thing to do each time? If you did, big cheers for you!

If you chose some of the other answers, try to think about Harry's choices to help you to be honest from now on. Then it will be big smiles all round!

And remember – if it's not yours, hand it over!

How to use this book

This book can be used by a grown-up and a child together. It is based on common situations in which any child might be tempted to be dishonest. Invite your child to talk about each of the choices. Ask questions such as 'Why do you think Harry should give the money back to the man who dropped it?'.

Discuss the wrong choices, as well as the right ones, with your child. Describe what is happening in the following pictures and talk about what the wrong and right choices might be.

- Taking things from other people is dishonest. Hand back something that isn't yours.

- Stealing from a shop is against the law. Don't do it! You will get into trouble, and your parents will, too.

• It isn't okay to steal something just so you can give it as a present. Think of other ways to make people happy.

• Don't break things just because you can't have them. Ask to share and your friends might let you play with their toys, too.

Talk about the difference between right and wrong. Is there ever a time when taking might be the right thing to do? Help your child look for other options such as earning pocket money, making a present or simply showing how much they love someone by trying to be good.

Try to explain that sometimes it is easier to be dishonest, but that stealing makes you feel bad about yourself. Making the right decision gives you a much happier feeling inside. Explain that it can also help you to feel better if you are honest about your emotions.

Glossary

borrow   when someone lets you take or use something of theirs for a short time

earning   being given money for doing jobs

honest   telling the truth

mistake   getting something wrong

muddle   confusion or a mess

pocket money   money children are given by their family, sometimes in return for doing jobs

price tag   a label put on something in a shop to show how much you must pay for it

proud   feeling very pleased with yourself or with someone else

realises   knows or understands

sharing   allowing others to use your things

stealing   taking something that does not belong to you

Index

Titles in the series

ISBN: 978 0 7502 6644 4

Like all children, Carlos sometimes does things that are wrong, and doesn't come clean. He has lots of choices to make – but which are the TRUTHFUL ones?

ISBN: 978 0 7502 6642 0

Like all children, Charlie sometimes feels a little scared. He has lots of choices to make – but which are the BRAVE ones?

ISBN: 978 0 7502 6645 1

Like all children, Gertie sometimes plays a little dirty. We put Gertie on the spot with some tricky problems and ask her to decide what is FAIR!

ISBN: 978 0 7502 6643 7

Like all children, Harry sometimes takes things that don't belong to him. He has lots of choices to make – but which are the HONEST ones?